Above: *Part of a row of coining presses installed in the Royal Mint, Llantrisant, South Wales, in 1970.*

COINS AND MINTING

Denis R. Cooper
TD, BSc, CEng, FIMechE

Shire Publications Ltd

CONTENTS

Introduction 3

Hammered coin, 700 BC to AD 1500 4

The first coining machines,
1500 to 1800 10

Mass production of coins,
1800 to 1939 21

Coin production today 29

Glossary 31

Places to visit 32

Further reading 32

Published in 1996 by Shire Publications Ltd, Cromwell House, Church Street, Princes Risborough, Buckinghamshire HP27 9AA, UK. Copyright © 1983 by Denis R. Cooper. First published 1983; second edition 1990, reprinted 1996. Shire Album 106. ISBN 0 7478 0069 3. Denis R. Cooper is hereby identified as the author of this work in accordance with Section 77 of the Copyright, Designs and Patents Act 1988.

Printed in Great Britain by CIT Printing Services, Press Buildings, Merlins Bridge, Haverfordwest, Dyfed SA61 1XF.

British Library Cataloguing in Publication Data. A catalogue record for this book is available from the British Library.

ACKNOWLEDGEMENTS
Acknowledgement is gratefully given to the following for their help in the loan of illustrative material and other assistance: British Museum, Colchester Museum, the Colchester Archaeological Trust, Danish National Museum, Swedish National Museum, Dr Leypold of Vienna, Birmingham Assay Office, International Nickel Company; to Roy Kilby, artist, for the sketch on page 11, and above all to my wife for her endless help and forbearance.

Cover: *The reverse of a commemorative medal issued by a Scandinavian mint illustrating a typical seventeenth-century screw press in operation.*

Chinese 'spade money', typical of east Asian coins. They were castings and therefore did not offer much security.

Part of a frieze in the House of the Vettii at Pompeii, in which cupids are depicted making coin.

INTRODUCTION

The words *money* and *mint* have a common origin: they derive from the Roman word for money, *moneta*, which is also described as a 'surname of Juno', in whose temple Roman money was regularly coined. This word in various forms can be traced throughout European languages. The French call their mint *La Monnaie*; in Spanish-speaking countries it is called *Moneda* and in Portuguese it is *Moeda*. In England, Germany and Scandinavia the word for the place where coins are made has become *Mint*, *Munz* and *Mynt*. In the English language *money* has been retained as the collective word describing not only coins but currency in many forms.

Coins were minted long before the days of Juno's temple. We are told by the ancient Greek writer Herodotus that the Lydians in Asia Minor (now Turkey), under King Croesus (550 BC), were the first nation to use gold and silver coins to buy and sell goods. Before this time, authorised electrum ingots had been used as a medium of exchange. (Electrum was a naturally occurring alloy which was usually composed of 80 per cent silver and 20 per cent gold.) These officially issued ingots showed only their place of origin and their composition, and each piece had to be weighed to ascertain its value, but they were not true coins. It was not until the Lydians developed the art of impressing designs on the faces of uniform pieces of metal that we have anything which satisfies the definition of *coin* – that is an object, normally of metal, of a known composition, of specified weight and therefore of known value, each piece bearing the seal or stamp of a recognised issuing authority. This definition applies to western civilisation, where, for most purposes, the seal has been the major sign of authority. Early Chinese coins were usually cast and they were mostly in the shape of fishes and spades and are referred to as such.

In the following chapters the methods of making the metal pieces and their preparation will be described first, and then the preparation of the tools for the actual *striking*. Methods have gradually developed through the centuries, but in any minting process the metals and the tools are the essentials. There have been four stages of development: (1) by far the longest was the initial period from the Lydian times of over 2500 years ago until the fifteenth and sixteenth centuries, when (2) fundamental improvements were introduced and manually operated machines became available; (3) with the coming of the industrial revolution at the end of the eighteenth century automatic machinery was introduced; and (4) the latest period which began soon after the Second World War, when the use of banking and credit facilities had the effect of turning nearly all modern coins into tokens. Such a token coinage has very little *intrinsic worth* as it no longer contains its stated value in the quantity of the metal from which it is made. However, there continue to be important technical developments in the production of today's coins.

3

Clay moulds for coin casts found at Colchester in the 1930s and dating from about 100 BC. The hollows appear to have been arranged in seven rows of seven, with one extra, so as to produce fifty casts.

HAMMERED COIN, 700 BC TO AD 1500

The first coins were made using the simplest tools. By 550 BC the Lydians, among other peoples, were able to produce iron and non-ferrous metals; these latter were chiefly gold, silver and copper. Metalworkers also knew how to alloy and mix these metals and knew that a furnace was essential to operate such processes using charcoal for fuel. The coiner melted the required mix of metals to a high temperature in a covered clay *crucible* placed in a clay-lined furnace, and the right temperature was probably judged by observing the changing colours of the *melt*. At the appropriate moment the molten metal (now an alloy) was poured into small dish-shaped clay moulds. This was a sure way of obtaining good metal, as the 'slag', or impurities and dirt in the ores, floated to the top

and was easily removed. (The iron sections of Darby's Iron Bridge over the river Severn were made in this way over two thousand years later!) The *casts* or buttons of metal so formed could then be hammered into the shape of a disc. Heat was used to keep the metal soft, and often the cast was held on edge and hammered, to remove as much as possible of the *flash* or rough edge. This flash remaining on the coin edge is sometimes helpful in enabling us to date coins made in ancient Mediterranean mints.

The shaped cast had now become the *blank* on which the design could be hammered to form a coin.

Suitably engraved *dies* were required to impress each prepared blank with a seal of authority and these dies had to be

4

Decadrachma of Syracuse, about 500 BC. This very beautiful coin was struck on to a hot blank and the remains of the flash on the edges are obvious near both the top and bottom of the coin. There are also small cracks round the edges where the metal would have cooled more quickly. (1¼ times actual size.)

capable of impressing many blanks.

Unfortunately very few of these early tools have been found so that our detailed knowledge of their composition is limited, but we do know that initially bronze alloys of 80 per cent copper and 20 per cent tin were often used. The coin blanks were heated to soften them and were struck with the already engraved dies while still hot. This practice was widespread, and it explains the high *relief* of early Mediterranean coins, because cold metal could not have been pressed so deeply into the recesses of the designs on the dies. These bronze dies were cast in the form of cylinders about 4 inches (100 mm) long and with a diameter equal to that of the blanks to be struck into a coin. The design was cut into one end of the cylinder with hand engraving tools very similar to those used today. As the impression on the die became worn, it could be recut, perhaps several times. In order to use dies for striking both sides of a coin at the same

time, the lower or bottom die was usually fixed in a block of wood with the engraved face uppermost, virtually forming an anvil. The blank to be struck was placed on this die, and the top die – engraving downwards – was held over the blank, and the whole assembly was struck a powerful blow with a heavy hammer. If the coin was struck while hot, the coiner (or moneyer) must have had a small furnace adjacent to his anvil, with the supply of blanks being kept hot, perhaps in a bed of charcoal, to prevent discolouration. If any quantity of coins was being struck the dies would become hot and tarnished and, to prevent this, the coiner probably had a piece of tallow to wipe them and keep them clean.

Gradually bronze dies were superseded by a form of iron that could be hardened and ultimately by steel. These introductions were slow, because ironworking required still higher temperatures than those needed for bronze and the process was more complex, although iron had been *smelted*

A beautifully engraved copper sestertius of the Hadrian period, about AD 120, struck in Rome. Very few Roman coins were struck in Britain. (1¼ times actual size.)

Above left: *Top and bottom dies used for hammer striking. In medieval England the bottom die was known as a 'pile' and the top as a 'trussel'.*

Above right: *A stained glass window in Milan Cathedral showing the Danish saint Elegius and an assistant striking coins.*

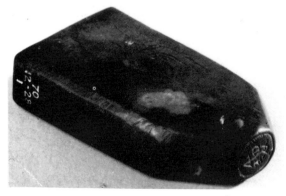

Left: *A touchstone found in the west of England, with a goldsmith's mark of the sixteenth century, and showing touchmarks on the flat surface.*

for at least five hundred years before the production of the first coins. Smelted iron was obtained by heating the ore with charcoal, and it is comparatively impure with a high carbon content. A method of purification by *puddling* eliminated most of the carbon and so produced wrought iron which was more easily worked. Die bodies could be made from this wrought iron, but owing to slag inclusions this metal could not be engraved. Steel made from melted material which contained no slag was available in small quantities and this could be engraved. After a long period a method was developed for welding small discs of steel to form tips on wrought iron shanks. This tip was engraved, *carburised* by heating in glowing charcoal and hardened by quenching. This treatment produced a thin layer of hardened steel suitable for striking the blanks when they were cold, and this avoided the overheating of the dies as well as the difficulties of keeping the blanks hot. These developments led to the introduction of thinner and larger coins.

Another fundamental function was *assaying*. It was vitally important to be able to determine the precious metal contents of alloys used for coinage: and the earliest assayers did this by using a 'touchstone'. This was a *siliceous* stone found in Asia Minor and sometimes known as *Lapis Lydia*. Assayers made 'touch needles' of known gold or silver composition and with these made marks on a touchstone; these marks provided a basis for comparison with similar marks made by the alloy to be proved or tested. It was possible to assay compositions to 2 or 3 per cent accuracy in this way and enabled the intrinsic value of coin to be demonstrated, so ensuring public confidence in the coinage.

Pure silver and pure gold were obtained by heating the ore bearing the precious metal with lead in a small container made from the ash of burnt bones. During the heating the lead combined with any other metals present and became absorbed into the container, leaving a nugget of pure silver or gold ready for working. Knowledge of these processes was the basis of the moneyers' craft, and a moneyer was an important person for any authority to employ.

Gold or silver in the form of coin has always been worth more by weight than in any other form. The difference between the value of a gold coin and the value of the same weight of gold in ingot form became known as 'seignorage', which the local issuing authority, frequently a temple and later a church or abbey, claimed as a right. It provided a substantial income, and the moneyer received his share. A good moneyer was literally 'worth his weight in gold'.

The craft of coinmaking was a closely guarded secret, and information was not readily passed, even between moneyers. Coins produced in areas of Greek and Roman influence were superior in workmanship to those produced elsewhere: the coins of Celtic cultures show this markedly, and as the Celts left no evidence of a written language of their own Greek or Roman inscriptions are often found on their otherwise distinctive coins. It was from the Mediterranean cultures that the Celts probably obtained much of their coinmaking technology, although their skilful iron and bronze workmanship is beyond dispute.

There were many small variations in the methods of manufacture during this early period and a study of ancient coins indicates a wide range of ways of cutting and adjusting blanks before striking, together with different methods of aligning dies. Some moneyers used an alignment

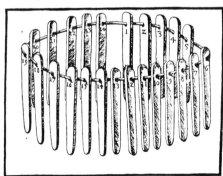

Touch needles of gold from 1 to 24 carat, as illustrated by the sixteenth-century metallurgist Agricola.

collar while others hinged the top and bottom dies together. Many faulty coins were produced and have been found, and from these we have been able to discover some of their mistakes. Two typical examples are double striking, and placing two blanks together between the dies so that each of the two coins received an impression on only one side.

Anglo-Saxon coins are particularly interesting for their quality and uniformity; also the moneyers were allowed to leave an identifying mark on their products. In England the basis of the coinage was laid down during the eighth, ninth and tenth centuries. Alfred the Great organised the mints and authorised who should engrave dies and who could strike coins. In AD 982 King Aethelstan decreed that all mints must obtain their dies from London, so giving security and establishing central control over design.

One of the most notable moneyers was Godwine, or Godpin; he engraved dies and struck coins for King Canute of England (who was also King Cnut of Denmark) and for King Swein Forkbeard, also of Denmark, as well as striking coins for other Scandinavian kings of that time. If, as we suppose, it was the same man, Godwine must have been a frequent traveller across the North Sea around the year 1000! During this period it became the custom to identify not only the moneyers but also the mints where the coins were struck. Composition was specified and the designs became more uniform. Churches which had been allowed to issue their own coins now lost their seignorage rights, but nevertheless the symbol of the cross remained part of the design, together with the king's effigy, his name and the word *rex*.

Coinciding with this improved administration came better methods of manufacture, and coins became more sophisticated. Moneyers cast thin strips or plates of coinage metal in open moulds which were depressions in a clay bed. These casts (or ingots) of alloy were then *cleaned* and hammered out to coin-blank thickness. This progressive hammering required skill and craftsmanship, because the metal needed

Above: *A Celtic coin with a typical horse design and bearing Latin inscriptions on both sides. This is a 'Commius' (a Celtic king) issued for his son Verica. (1½ times actual size.)*

Above: *Hinged coin dies; the blank was placed between the engraved faces as when sealing. This method aligned the dies but did not locate the blank centrally.*

Above: *A coin of King Cnut with the names of the moneyer and mint in the inscription around the cross on the reverse. (1½ times actual size.)*

8

A drawing of the mint at Halle, Austria. Maximillian, the son Ferdinand I, is receiving instruction in coin production. The operations are: (left) a blank annealing furnace; (left forward) cutting blanks from sheet; (centre) beating cast sheet to blank thickness; (right) striking the coin. The Mint Master controls operations by weighing and recording issues of metal to the workers. The chest, relatively small, could be a 'pyx' chest for samples set aside for verification. The British verification ceremony known as the Trial of the Pyx has origins as far back as the late thirteenth century.

frequent *annealing* to keep it soft.

After hammering, the plate was cut into strips about the same width as the diameter of the coin blank, the strips were then cut into squares, and the corners trimmed until each square became nearly round. A well known illustration shows minting operations reputed to be in Maximillian's mint at Halle in Austria, about 1480. The cast plates, blank-cutting and coining operations are clearly shown, with the furnace for annealing the blanks on one side. Unfortunately there are many operations not depicted here, although we can find some of them in other pictures of the times. There were many mints in Europe in the middle ages, where the processes were still the carefully guarded secrets of the moneyers.

Alfred the Great's triumphal 'London Monogram' coin, celebrating his conquest of that city in AD 886 and consequent mastery of England.

THE FIRST COINING MACHINES, 1500 TO 1800

Late in the fifteenth century changes were made to manufacturing processes. Manually operated machines were being developed which improved the tools available for making coins. A degree of specialisation came with better furnaces, new rolling mills, and blanking and coining presses. Mints became larger and departmentalised in a way which has remained until modern times. During the renaissance period artists in Florence were studying perspective and structure and this led to the application of the new ideas on constructional principles, including the design of two main types of coining presses.

About 1508 the Florentine artist Bramante struck medals in a screw press and some thirty years later a compatriot, Benvenuto Cellini, struck coins and left a full description of the screw press which he had used. He found that the new press produced better coins and wore the dies less and he wrote: 'for every one struck by the coiners, twenty are stamped with the screw.' This achievement by Cellini and his successors was bitterly opposed by traditional moneyers, an attitude typical of industrial innovation at any period. Gradually the power of screw presses increased during the sixteenth and seventeenth centuries; by 1671 a detailed drawing of a press was made in Middelburg in the Netherlands and this design is typical of all screw presses made during the next century. The coining dies used in these presses had square bodies, and the top and bottom dies were each held in a four-screw chuck, but no collar was used to hold the coin blank. The chuck holding the top die was held up to the screw by two hook-shaped springs and it was prevented from turning by the square holes in the die plates.

At this time it was relatively easy to make a good screw but making the nut needed to guide it was more difficult. The problem was overcome by covering the screw with a dressing made of oil, powdered bone ash and charcoal, and placing it in a mould into which molten bronze was poured. The dressing on the screw allowed for shrinkage during the pouring but produced a nut which fitted closely enough to

An artist's impression of a late eighteenth-century screw coining press as used in the Kremnica mint in Slovakia.

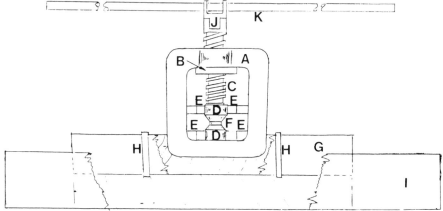

An interpretation of Benvenuto Cellini's description of his first screw press. His information does not make clear how the dies were held in place. Key: A, iron frame 1¹/₂ by 3 inches (38 by 76 mm) in section; B, bronze nut; C, screw 2¹/₄ inches (57 mm) in diameter; D, top and bottom dies; E, wedges fixing dies; F, blank; G, recessed timber beam; H, iron clamps; I, timber baulk in ground; J, iron pole carrier; K, operating pole.

match the thread on the screw.

As the use of screw presses spread and technical knowledge increased designs continually improved. The screw press at the mint in Kremnica, now in Slovakia, is a good example and is illustrated. The illustration clearly shows collars, but we have very little evidence of how these were used or fitted in the machines, and especially of how coins were extracted after striking. Prior to their use many coiners lost their fingers as they placed the blank on the bottom die and the screw holding the top die descended too quickly. We have reports that a screw press with a team of four operators plus a coiner could produce sixty coins a minute, and that each team worked for about twenty minutes.

The basic design of the second machine introduced into coining was a special type of rolling mill, and this is first mentioned in Leonardo da Vinci's notebooks. The *obverse* and *reverse* designs to be impressed on the coins were engraved on to the faces of each of a pair of rolls; there were then two possibilities: the designs could be rolled either directly on to prepared blanks, or continuously on to a strip. In the latter case the coin would then have to be cut out of the strip. Suitably engraved rolls could have impressed two or more designs at once. This method differed from striking coin in a press as the metal-shaping force only acted progressively along a narrow band of contact and not over the whole surface of the blank. This meant that the force required was very much less than that for striking and so a larger blank could be

An Austrian thaler of 1506 produced by the rolling mill method. The coins are not circular, the vertical axis being about 1 millimetre longer than the horizontal.

Right: *Three rolling mill machines of the sixteenth century, now in Czesky Kremlov, Czech Republic. The two on the right are the Taschenwerke type.*

Below left: *Engraved rolls of the Walzenwerke type. These could have been used in a machine similar to the one standing on the ground in the photograph above. They could roll only strip and not individual blanks.*

Below right: *A pair of Taschenwerke engraved dies for insertion in rolls to produce either individual coins or a strip of coins ready for cutting. The upper die is shown at right angles to the lower for purposes of comparison.*

Above: *A sixteenth-century view of the silver and gold mine with the mint at Kremnica. The mint is in front of the church and still stands on the same site today in this picturesque walled town.*

Left: *The famous Austrian numismatic masterpiece, the 1780 Maria Theresia thaler, still used today as a trade dollar in the Middle East.*

rolled into a coin. Also, during the sixteenth century there was an increasing public demand for large silver coins, and so the new *Walzenwerke*, or rolling machines, were widely used. They remained popular for about two hundred years, and European mints developed the technique and also made modifications. The most important of these was called *Taschenwerke*, or pocket work, and involved the insertion of specially shaped dies into recesses on the rolls. Three rolling machines are illustrated which were used by the Counts of Cesky Kremlov, now in the Czech Republic, and they were probably similar to those on which the first *Joachimsthalers* were made. In 1519 the Count of Schlick was granted the right to make coins using the metal from the rich silver mine in the Joachimsthal, or Joachim's Valley. He is-

sued *grossen Groschen* (literally 'large groats'), which became known as *thalers*, and it is from this last word that the name *dollar* derives. The town of Joachimsthal is now called Jachymov and lies about 50 miles (80 km) north of Pilsen.

The rolling machines were used extensively in the mints which were built near the gold and silver mines in central Europe. Perhaps the best known is that at Kremnica, where the mint was established in 1328 by King Karl Robert; it was here that the rolling method was developed to its fullest extent. A machine and tools can be seen in the museum of this small Slovakian town in the Southern Tatra Mountains, and silver is still mined in the nearby hills. Coins were produced here in this way until about 1750.

As a result of the connection between

14

Right: *A sketch of the Taschenwerke mill, showing how it could have been used. The dies (not found) went in pockets at AA and the rolling motion was about the centres BB. It was clamped to a base C.*

Below: *Charles I Irish farthings made by the Walzenwerke method. Each roll had nine die engravings and the measured distance between the two sets of dots indicates that the rolls must have been 52 millimetres (2 inches) in diameter. The two ends marked A correspond.*

Left: *An example of Swedish copper 'plate' money, equal to a thaler in value, but 250 times its weight. Note the use of the word 'daler'.*

Right: *The lower part of a horse gin (above) where the crown wheel drives the two lantern wheels shown in the lower section. The right-hand wheel drives two spur gears which drive the rolling mills B and B. The left-hand wheel drives the more powerful mill A. Its associated spur gear appears to be unnecessary.*

the Austrian and Spanish kingdoms in the sixteenth century, the know-how of the Austrians passed to the Spanish town of Segovia, where the Walzenwerke rolls were driven by a waterwheel. The Taschenwerke machine was already being used in Spain, and one was found in Seville by an English collector and brought to England, where it was held in the British Museum. It could have been used only for the production of small coins. With this machine the frame of the press rocked so that it is often described as a 'rocker press'. As late as the reign of Charles I, the Walzenwerke method was tried in England, and again in Scotland in 1639, and a large number of 'Richmond Farthings' are in the British Museum coin collection – there are both finished pieces and impressed strips awaiting cutting. These machines, however, were finally abandoned in favour of the screw presses.

Because of the ever increasing value of silver and the successive wars in northern Europe, copper became widely used for coinage. This metal was mined extensively in Scandinavia and was therefore comparatively cheap, and one of the solutions to the problem of providing sufficient coins was the issue of 'plate money'. These plates were extremely heavy, so that a horse and cart were often necessary to carry a week's takings to the bank, and in due course this led to the issue of bonds and transferable notes. The word *daler* (pronounced 'dahler') appears on the plate money – already the *thaler* has undergone a change towards *dollar*.

Meanwhile methods of blank preparation were steadily improving. The alloys could now be melted in a better furnace using bellows to provide the draught. The metals were placed in a covered container inside the furnace and the container was removed with tongs and put into a ladle ring. From this the molten metal could be poured into *chill* cast iron moulds, and, when cold, the ingots so formed could be removed. These ingots were cleaned and any slag remaining at the top was sheared off. Rolling mills, in appearance and action very like old-fashioned domestic mangles, squeezed the metal down to the right thickness for the blanks and were sometimes driven by waterwheel and sometimes by horse or mule *gins*.

All metal hardens when it is worked, and there is a stage in rolling when it becomes necessary to soften the strip by annealing it. Coinage metals must not be ex-

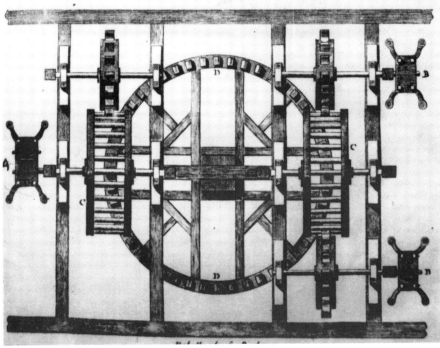

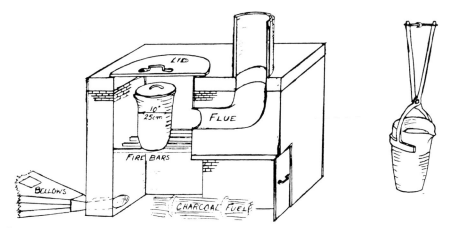

Sectional view of a crucible melting furnace, and (right) the tongs for transferring the crucible from furnace to tilter.

posed to air while they are hot or they tarnish, and they must therefore be annealed in such a way that they are protected from contact with air. In the period we are considering, this was done by heating the strip under a bed of charcoal, or in clay-sealed boxes in a furnace. The temperature varied between about 900°F and 1400°F (500°C and 750°C). After rolling the strip to the required thickness, the blanks were cut out, often using a simple hand press. The operator swung the operating lever with one hand while feeding pieces of strip with the other. The final rolling after annealing would have hardened the strip again, so that the cut blanks now needed annealing,

because blanks must always be as soft as possible for striking. They were then cleaned, traditionally in argol, or tartaric acid – a by-product of winemaking. As soon as the blanks were dry they were ready for striking.

An important change took place in the preparation of the dies simultaneously with all the other improvements: a *piece punch* was engraved with the effigy to be used on the coin and, using the screw press, a *negative* impression was made in a *die blank*, and the inscriptions of names and dates were then engraved around the effigy, also in negative. Coinmaking had become a work of art as well as a craft.

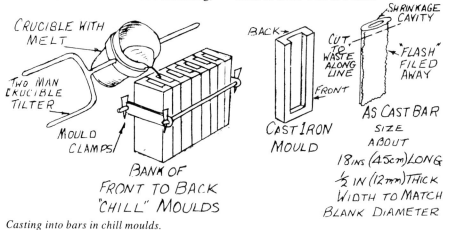

Casting into bars in chill moulds.

18

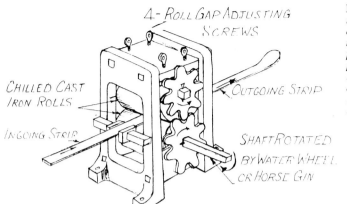

4- ROLL GAP ADJUSTING SCREWS

CHILLED CAST IRON ROLLS

INGOING STRIP

OUTGOING STRIP

SHAFT ROTATED BY WATER WHEEL OR HORSE GIN

Left: Details of the rolling mills shown on page 17. These mills had very little power so that many passes were required to thin the strip. The drawing shows the rolling of cast bar to blank thickness.

Right: A manually operated blank cutting-out press, cutting out blanks from strip.

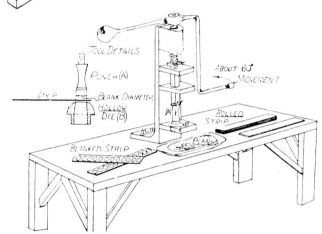

TOOL DETAILS

PUNCH (A)

STRIP

BLANK DIAMETER

HOLLOW DIE (B)

ABOUT 60° MOVEMENT

ROLLED STRIP

BLANKS

BLANKED STRIP

Below: Brick-built blank annealing furnace, charcoal fired. The view is cut away vertically along X and Y.

A: FIREBRICK CHAMBER LINING
B: CAST IRON BARS
C: RESTING FRAME
D: LUTED BLANK BOX
E: CLAY SEALED LID
F: FLUE
G: STOKE HOLE
H: HEARTH
K: ACCESS FOR CHARGING
L: ACCESS CLOSURE PLATE

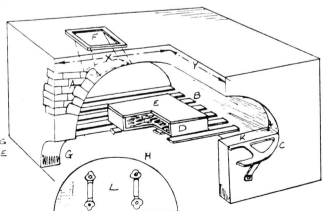

Piece punches for making uniform impressions on die blanks, eliminating the need to cut the whole design completely by hand on every working die.

Matthew Boulton FRS, jeweller, brassware manufacturer, philanthropist, benevolent industrialist and partner of James Watt. Boulton can be described as the father of modern coinage.

Matthew Boulton's Soho Works, Birmingham, where condensing steam engines were first built and the first automatic coining presses were made.

MASS PRODUCTION OF COINS, 1800 TO 1939

Matthew Boulton initiated the change from manually operated to power-driven coining machines and was the first to introduce a degree of automation. Boulton owned the Soho Works in Birmingham, where he produced buttons and other small brass goods. He worked in partnership with James Watt, the famous steam engine designer, and Boulton was therefore able to install one of Watt's improved steam engines to provide power for his machinery. He became interested in currency problems when the Royal Mint in London was failing lamentably to supply the national requirements of bronze coin, of which there was a dearth. Privately issued tokens were becoming widely used and equally widely abused, and workpeople were paid in bronze tokens whose purchasing powers were less than half their face values. Often the tokens could only be used at nominated shops and tradesmen so nominated refused to recognise the face value of the token and would only supply goods worth a substantially smaller amount. Boulton was very conscious of the distress and poverty this practice caused, for he was an employer with advanced views, and he gave much

thought to the problem of the lack of bronze coins. He approached the government and obtained a contract to mint 'Cartwheel Pennies' dated 1797. These were large copper coins each made from a pennyworth of copper and their production was an important step for Boulton, because the number of coins required gave him the incentive to drive his coining press by 'steam', as it was then described. In fact he was the first person to construct a power-driven, automatic press. He used his steam engine to produce a vacuum. This activated a mechanism to rotate the screw of a coining press. Boulton had already made improvements to the earlier designs of screw presses and he linked in a mechanism to operate the swinging arm previously handled by a team of men. In 1871 Ansell, a Royal Mint employee, published a book which included an engraving showing how Boulton's plan worked to operate a number of presses, and also how it allowed the blanks to be fed automatically between the dies while each previously struck coin was ejected.

Boulton and his contemporaries made much of the simplicity of the operation of his press. A boy could work it! First, how-

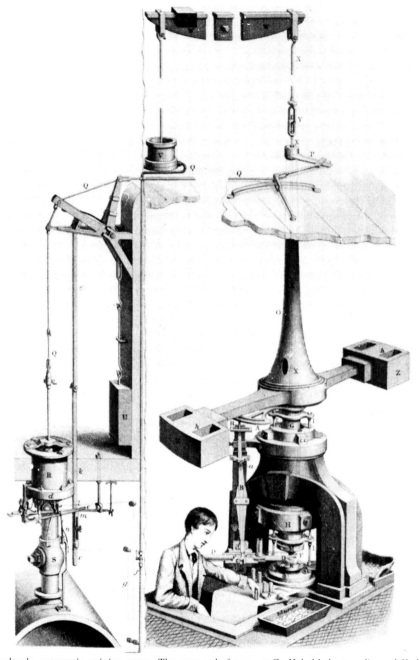

Boulton's automatic coining press. The screw shaft was at G; H held the top die and K the bottom die; the arm Z was driven by the vacuum created in the cylinder R. The automatic feed mechanism was driven by the cam A which actuated the bar BB and the sliders DD. Piled blanks were placed in a feed tube between C and D, fed between the dies and ejected at F.

Above: *Boulton's copper 'Cartwheel Penny', struck in the Soho Works.*

Below: *Uhlhorn's knuckle (or knee-action) press. The crankshaft and connecting rod recipro-cated the sway lever. The column and hammer lever moved up and down together; they were held in position by the weights. The feed mechanism, similar to Boulton's, rested on the feed table and was driven by a linkage from the crankshaft. The salmon lever linkage reciprocated the feed table, extracting the struck coin from the collar. One cycle of operation was effected in one revolution of the crankshaft.*

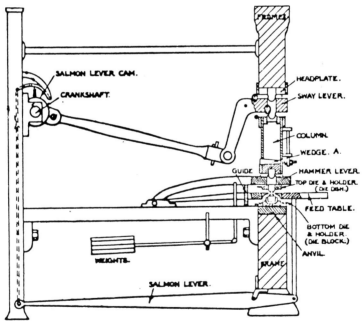

ever, the 'boy' had to flatten any curved blanks to prevent them jamming the feed mechanism – hence the hammer on the bench beside the piles of coin. Boulton equipped the Soho Mint with his presses and then received orders from the Royal Mint in London, and subsequently from numerous overseas mints, for his automatic presses. The records indicate that about seventy-five were supplied in all. Although the machines fulfilled their specification regarding automation and improved finish,

23

they could fairly be criticised. The engineer James Murdoch Napier, reporting in 1871, said: 'the press... was complicated, scattered and unhandy, reaching into three departments and requiring a foundation of great solidity and special construction of building.' The noise and vibration were described by some as 'intolerable.'

By this time other designs had been produced. In 1817 a patent had been taken out by a German, Diedrich Uhlhorn, for a 'knuckle' press which worked on a lever principle. As with screw presses there was a main frame but with a larger aperture, or window, and the lower die rested on the base of the opening as before. The mechanism carrying the upper die consisted of three links known as the 'sway lever', the 'column' and the 'hammer lever', and the die was fixed to the underside of the last. Both the feed motion for the blanks and the ejection motion for the struck coins were very similar to those fitted by Boulton to his screw presses. When starting up the Uhlhorn press, the operator had to run a flywheel up to sufficient speed and to engage a clutch; long levers were provided to enable this to be done, reaching from the back to the front of the machine. A smooth start at the lowest possible speed required some skill and careful timing. Uhlhorn's press was probably the most commonly used model until modern times. Over two hundred machines were made by the original company and over three hundred and fifty by the chief licensees, Ralph Heaton and Sons of Birmingham, and their successors. Its popularity was largely due to the ease of its manufacture and the fact that it

Right: *Types of edge designs: A, common milling for which the coinage collar has a milled bore and the metal of the blank is pressed out by the dies so that the edges are impressed by the collar; B and C, edge milling rolled in after the blank was struck: this was an unusual method of the eighteenth century; D, security edge milling, a combination of a narrow edge design deeply impressed into the blank edge followed by a normal striking operation using a collar with a milled bore; E, a typical example of a combination of letters and design rolled into the blank edge followed by a normal striking operation in a plain collar.*

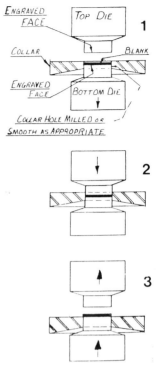

Above: *Essential steps in coin striking. 1: The bottom die descends to form a recess to receive a blank for coining. 2: The top die descends and its pressure coins the blank. Both dies and collar are made from hardened steel. Coining pressures vary from 50 to 100 tons per square inch, depending on alloy and design. 3: The top die returns and the bottom die rises, ejecting the coin from the collar.*

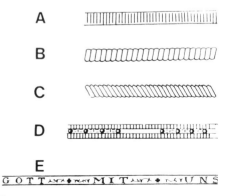

Above: *Thonnelier's knuckle press of 1830. This press is in the Musée des Arts et Métiers, Paris. It has Uhlhorn features because the two men worked together, but in many ways Thonnelier's press was a very much improved design.*

Below: *A bank of modified Uhlhorn presses installed in the Royal Dutch Mint about 1900.*

did not require a complex casting for the frame. Its success was a consequence of the newly available good quality steel forgings for the knuckle parts. The operating speed stabilised at about ninety strikes per minute and the presses could be used to strike all types of coin – plain-edged, lettered or milled-edge, shaped, and also the special raised-letter edge known as *virole brisé* which had to be struck in split collars. The presses were made in three sizes, the largest one capable of striking coins up to $1\frac{1}{2}$ inches (38 mm) diameter.

A number of manufacturers copied the Uhlhorn machines with minor modifications, but in 1830 another designer adapted the knuckle-lever principle to an entirely new concept. This was the Thonnelier press, first introduced in the Hotel de le Monnaie (the Paris mint), and it employed new ideas for the blank feeding and coin ejecting movements, and also for the die fixtures. Again many manufacturers copied the new design, adding their own variations, and perhaps the best known was the Birmingham firm of Taylor and Challen Ltd. The German firm of Schuler made presses which combined the new frame and knuckle arrangements with the old feed motion of the Uhlhorn press.

These latest press designs did not change to any great extent until after 1945; coins

Above: *Pistrucci's 'George and Dragon' design used on sovereign and half-sovereign reverses for over 150 years.*

Left: *The pantograph reducing machine, which copied the artist's design (right-hand side) to the desired coin size (left-hand side).*

Below: *Casting bars into chill moulds in the Royal Dutch Mint about 1900. The metal is melted in the three tilting furnaces on the right. The middle furnace is heating in this picture.*

Tandem rolling mills, with a common drive, in the Royal Mint, London, about 1900; they were made by Maudslay Sons and Field. Spare rolls are held in the racks on the back wall.

were produced at speeds of up to 120 a minute and the largest mints had up to fifty presses installed, dependent upon their coinage requirements. The annual output of the USA mint of coins of all types was about five hundred million before 1939. Other countries' productions were in proportion to their population and wealth.

Other developments in industry during the nineteenth century led to changes in minting operations. The new automatic coining presses required large quantities of dies. Fortunately, Huntsman of Sheffield, in the middle of the eighteenth century, while searching for a better steel for clock springs, discovered *crucible steel*, containing about one per cent carbon, and this was found to make very superior coinage dies. It was relatively soft when annealed, but when heated and quenched its surface became very hard indeed. Complete dies of this new steel could now be struck from a *master* of the same material. This allowed for all of the coin design to be produced in relief, so forming the *master punch* which was used to strike complete *incuse* (or negative) designs on to die blanks. In practice a negative design called a *matrix* was first hand-engraved in the steel and then hardened. By using the now higher-powered screw presses a *raised* (or positive) punch called a *patrix* was impressed into the steel die blanks, and this could be used to strike

many dies. Quick arithmetic shows that if the patrix struck a thousand dies and each die struck an average of fifty thousand coins, one patrix had a potential of fifty million identical coins. The matrix could also produce many patrices and, providing that the engraving did not need to be touched up, the theoretical potential of identical coins from one original became enormous. Small changes such as dates could be made with a minimum of handwork but inevitably this produced problems, the major one being that at each step the diameter of the dies tended to increase, sometimes between 0.2 and 0.5 per cent. Such an effect was cumulative, and an example of such increases was the Australian coinage; the patrices were supplied by London to the Royal Australian Mint, and the resulting penny and halfpenny coins were visibly larger than those made in London.

The second change made in die production was the introduction of the pantograph reducing machine. This could simultaneously both copy and reduce in size a large model directly on to the required steel. The model, whether positive or negative, was a bronze cast of the artist's plaster sculpture and is shown mounted on the right-hand side of the illustration. The die blank to be cut is mounted in the middle and a pivoting arrangement is on the left. The soft steel could be hardened after cut-

27

Above: *Hand-fed blanking presses in the Royal Dutch Mint, about 1900. The accuracy with which practised operators could feed the strip was remarkable.*

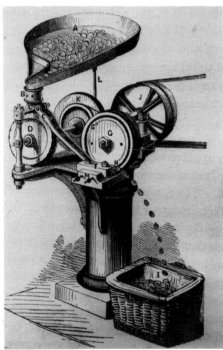

Left: *A typical rimming machine up-setting blank edges in the Royal Mint, London, about 1870; the principle is still used in today's machines.*

ting and then used to strike the matrix or patrix, as appropriate. This machine removed the highly skilled but tedious work of hand-engraving the dies, and more importantly it led to the production of identical designs in a range of diameters. It was introduced into the Royal Mint, London, in 1820 by Pistrucci, the engraver who was responsible for the well known George and Dragon design on gold sovereigns. The earliest machines of this type had been used in Italy for cutting cameos, and this had been Pistrucci's trade before he came to London.

As coke or town gas became available to fire the furnaces, these increased in size, together with the crucibles which were placed in them. The molten metal could now be poured into banks of 'chills' from which the *frozen* thin, rectangular castings could be withdrawn. These were about 2 inches (50 mm) wide, $\frac{1}{2}$ inch (12 mm) thick and 18 inches (450 mm) long. After *dressing*, the bars were rolled to the required thickness in small power-driven mills, and the resulting strips were then ready for cutting or 'blanking', when the blanks were stamped out to the size required for coining. At first the strips were skilfully fed by hand into the cutting press, but soon machines fed them forward in exactly predetermined amounts so that the maximum number of blanks was cut. These blanks now needed cleaning and this was done in rotating earthenware barrels, still using argol. Drying, followed by further 'barrelling', left the blanks with a good bright surface, but they needed one more processing before they were ready for striking; this was *rimming* or rolling between grooves, which ensured perfect size and roundness and also *upset* or thickened the edges of the blanks. Now they were ready for striking into coins in the automatic presses.

COIN PRODUCTION TODAY

Wars often increase the demand for coins and since the Second World War a high demand has been maintained. The total of all coin issued since 1945 has increased by about 10 per cent annually. Today's coins are mostly made from base metals, usually in alloys of copper, aluminium and nickel. Base metal currencies are far less expensive to maintain in circulation although they now have only token value. They are much cheaper to produce and they wear better than the softer precious metals. A few coins are made from gold and silver alloys but these are rarely used for day to day transactions.

There have been few radical changes in the methods of making coins but the larger mints now install sophisticated and automated machinery for many of the processes, while smaller mints often purchase blanks prepared for striking from specialist suppliers. Such suppliers regard coin blanks as only one of their many non-ferrous products, and it is a competitive business. In all mints there are now fast coining presses, sometimes striking over three hundred pieces a minute; there are special rimming machines and high-speed counting equipment, but the essential processes of alloying, melting, rolling, blanking and coining are fundamentally unchanged.

More significant has been the development of lamina or 'sandwich' materials to prevent abuses of the vending machines so much in use in modern societies. The first lamina coins were made from blanks cut out of 'clad' steel sheet and first used in Germany to overcome a shortage of copper. The coin faces were of brass or bronze, depending upon the denomination, but the steel was exposed on the outer edge between the thin layers of yellow metal. They proved to be most successful, are still in use today and unlikely to be changed.

This sandwich idea was extended to *cupro-nickel* coins in western Europe about 1960, because there was confusion and petty theft due to the coins of adjacent countries being identical in size and composition but very different in value. A coin-operated machine is unable to discriminate between the different face values of equally sized coins of identical metal fed into it. Pure nickel is magnetic, and this property was used to develop machines which would reject coins that did not give the correct response. A variety of sandwiched materials came into use, sometimes a pure nickel centre with outer layers of cupro-nickel, sometimes the other way round. Such coins were quickly accepted in Europe, but in Sweden and the USA there was a different problem because of the electrical conductivity of the silver coins then in circulation. These had become higher in value than their stated purchasing power and they were being illegally and very profitably melted down and the silver sold. In order to retain the appearance, and also to provide the same electrical conductivity required for their vending machines, these two countries produced coins made with a copper centre covered by a thin layer of silver. An examination of USA coin edges clearly

Right: *A section of a modern 'sandwich' coin, enlarged fifty times. The cladding (in this instance pure nickel) is the white strip on both surfaces. The crystalline structure of the centre shows clearly and is probably a copper-nickel alloy. This outer skin of nickel is magnetic and therefore easily detectable in most vending machines.*

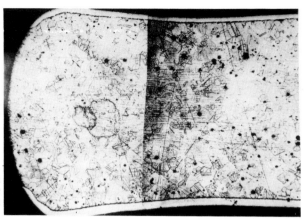

Below: *The two-piece, two-coloured Italian coin with a bronze centre and stainless steel outer ring introduced in 1982.*

shows the red centre. In Sweden the edges were silvered over, but it was an expensive process.

The foregoing are just a few examples of the new types of coinage, but perhaps the most interesting innovation was put into circulation in 1982. In Italy coins are being made from two separate parts, a bronze disc and a stainless steel ring, struck in-separably together. This is a most important development, because such coins offer a very high degree of security as they would be very difficult to counterfeit. They could revolutionise modern automated trading. This could be the most significant introduction of recent years, putting into practice an idea which had been suggested for the British coinage over a hundred years ago.

As coins become more difficult to counterfeit they can be used for higher values and remain a medium of exchange alongside paper money and credit cards. Being made of metal, they last for many years and still provide the cheapest form of currency to maintain, so that the era of plastic card transactions may not entirely replace the ancient craft of coinmaking.

Right: *A medal depicting the occasion in 1623 in Norway when a cow scraped its horn on a rock and a shepherd boy saw white shining metal exposed. This led to the establishment of a silver mine and a major mint which became the Royal Norwegian Mint in Kongsberg. Medal designed and engraved by Øivind Hansen in 1964.*

GLOSSARY

Anneal: to heat metal, usually to a red heat about 1300°F (750°C), to improve its workability.

Assay: to test or 'try' metals for composition by scientific methods.

Blank: the disc, normally circular, cut from a sheet of metal and prior to its final production as a coin.

Carburise: to introduce carbon into a piece of iron or steel using a furnace heated to about 800 °C.

Cast: the process of pouring molten metal into a mould, or, used as a noun, the *frozen* metal shape obtained after pouring.

Chill: a special type of mould, usually of cast iron, which is a good heat conductor and so quickly *freezes* the molten metal poured into it.

Clean: the activation of blanks in suitable liquids, such as dilute nitric or sulphuric acid, and a reducing agent to remove oxide so as to produce a bright metallic surface. Argol is also used, especially to brighten silver.

Collar: an accurately sized ring of metal used to hold the *blank* during striking. The hole is smooth-edged for plain-edged coins and vertically grooved for milled-edge coins.

Crucible: a heat-resistant vessel suitable to be placed in a melting furnace to hold the metals to be alloyed. Made of clay in olden times, but now made of graphite or silicon carbide.

Crucible steel: high quality steel melted in a crucible instead of by the Bessemer or other method. Huntsman's patented process was a major factor in the development of the Sheffield steel industry.

Cupro-nickel: alloys of copper and nickel; 75 per cent copper with 25 per cent nickel is mostly used for coinage.

Die: a tool for working metal; in coining it refers primarily to the tool carrying the final embossing design.

Die blank: the prepared steel forging from which a *die* is made by a striking or pressing operation, using a master working punch or *patrix*.

Dressing: the process of cleaning up metal *casts* by removing sand, mould oil and unwanted metal, leaving (in minting) a clean strip ready for rolling to size.

Fine ounce: a troy ounce (480 grains) of pure metal, usually of gold, silver or platinum.

Flash: the thin tongue of metal which flows between the adjacent faces of the two mould halves as the cast is poured.

Freeze: the solidification of liquid metal.

Gin: a mechanism for driving machinery by horse or water power – in fact an 'engine', also sometimes known as a 'whim'.

Incuse: a design which is cut in; a *negative* design.

Intrinsic worth or value: of a coin, one containing its real worth in metal; hence large pure silver and small gold coins.

Luted: sealed in a metal box with fireclay to prevent any entry of air and consequent oxidation or tarnishing.

Master: in coinage, the original engraved design from which all copies are obtained.

Master punch: a positive engraving the metal being cut away leaving the design up-standing, such as a reduction or hand-cut punch used as an original; a *patrix*.

Matrix: a *negative* engraving cut by hand or stamped in from a *master punch* or *patrix*.

Melt: a quantity of measured-out metal, melted and alloyed in a *crucible* in a melting furnace.

Negative: the incuse design, such as a *matrix* or working *die*.

Obverse: the side of a coin, arbitrarily chosen, which is the major side, but usually carrying the portrait.

Patrix: see *master punch*.

Piece punch: a portion, in positive, of a design used to impress parts of a design for the following *negative* stage in a *matrix* or working *die*.

Puddling: the manufacture in a furnace of wrought iron by removing the carbon from near-molten cast iron; working the iron mechanically with 'green' wood poles.

Raised-letter edge: a coin with a proud design or letters round its edge. This sort of edge is sometimes produced by a form of *rimming* before striking, and no *collar* is used in striking.

Relief: the embossing on a coin or coin tool design, the height usually being 1 to 2 per cent of the design diameter.

Reverse: the opposite side of the coin to the *obverse*.

Rimming: thickening or up-setting the edges of *blanks* before striking, sometimes impressing an *incuse* design into the edge of a blank before striking. Also called 'edge-marking'.

Siliceous: a compound containing silica, usually in a glass-like form.

Smelt: the use of a furnace to reduce metal compounds which are normally oxides, so as to obtain molten metal.

Up-set: working metal items to thicken them, e.g. nails from wire. In coining it refers to the thickening of the outside rim of the blank by rolling on edge between suitably grooved *dies*.

Virole brisé: often called 'split *collar* work' and invented about 1800 by Droz, a Swiss. The coinage *collar* is split into three segments and the inner side of each segment is impressed *incusely* with a design. When closed together to form a holding ring in the coining press, the *blank* edges are pressed into the design, so producing the *raised-letter edge*. This is a very sophisticated technique but it provides the highest degree of coin security because the three sections of the edge design are always in the same position in relationship to the *obverse* and *reverse* designs.

PLACES TO VISIT

Most county museums and site museums in the United Kingdom have early coins and exhibits relating to their manufacture. In other countries national museums all have a coin department and major technical museums have exhibits connected with minting. Many national mints receive visitors, by appointment. The museums listed below have exhibits of particular interest.

UNITED KINGDOM
Birmingham Museum of Science and Industry, Newhall Street, Birmingham B3 1RZ. Telephone: 0121-236 1661. (Matthew Boulton and the industrial revolution.)
Castle Museum, Castle Park, Colchester, Essex CO1 1TJ. Telephone: 01206 712939.

OTHER COUNTRIES
Alte Munze in Burg Hasegg, Hall-in-Tirol, Austria.
Badisches Landesmuseum, Schloss, 7500 Karlsruhe, West Germany.
Deutsches Museum, Museum Insel, 8000 München (Munich), Bavaria, West Germany.
Franklin Institute Science Museum, 20th Street and Parkway, Philadelphia, Pennsylvania 19103, USA. (A Thonnelier press can be seen working.)
Municipal Museum, Hellensteinovsky Dom, Namesty 1 Maja, Kremnica, Slovakia. (There are also mines and a mint at Kremnica.)
Musée des Arts et Métiers, 292 Rue Saint-Martin, 75141 Paris, France.
Museum of Industry and Technology, Mariahilferstrasse 212, 1140 Vienna 14, Austria.
Museum of the Paris Mint, Hôtel de la Monnaie, 11 Quai Conti, 75006 Paris, France.
Mynt Museum, Brukesgarten, Avesta, Sweden.
Mynt Museum, Kongsberg, Norway.

FURTHER READING

Cooper, Denis R. *The Art and Craft of Coinmaking*. Spink, 1988. ISBN 0907 605 27 3.
Cooper, Denis R. *Transactions* of the Newcomen Society, volume 47, 1974-6.
Craig, Sir John. *The Mint: A History of the London Mint from AD 287 to 1948*. Cambridge University Press, 1953.
Dickinson, H. W. *Matthew Boulton*. Cambridge University Press, 1937.
Grierson, Philip. *Numismatics*. Oxford University Press, 1975.